EARLY YEARS CARE
and EDUCATION

NVQ/SVQ LEVEL 2 WORKBOOK

Second Edition

CACHE

COUNCIL FOR AWARDS IN CHILDREN'S CARE AND EDUCATION
(incorporating CEYA and the NNEB)

Hodder & Stoughton

A MEMBER OF THE HODDER HEADLINE GROUP

Orders: please contact Bookpoint Ltd, 130 Milton Park, Abingdon, Oxon OX14 4SB. Telephone: (44) 01235 827720, Fax: (44) 01235 400454. Lines are open from 9.00–6.00, Monday to Saturday, with a 24 hour message answering service. You can also order through our website: www.hodderheadline.co.uk.

British Library Cataloguing in Publication Data

A catalogue record for this title is available from The British Library

ISBN 0 340 738138

First published 1999
Impression number   10   9   8   7   6   5   4   3
Year   2005   2004   2003

Cover illustration by Jane Taylor
Typeset by Wearset, Boldon, Tyne and Wear.
Printed in Great Britain for Hodder & Stoughton Educational, a division of Hodder Headline, 338 Euston Road London NW1 3BH by J. W. Arrowsmith Ltd, Bristol.

CONTENTS

ACKNOWLEDGEMENTS

The author, Alison Mitchell, would like to thank the Level 2 candidates at Oaklands College for their assistance in trialling some of the tasks in this book.

INTRODUCTION

This workbook is designed to help you to provide evidence of your underpinning knowledge and understanding of early years care and education in NVQ/SVQ at Level 2. The workbook is divided into 13 units. Each unit contains a variety of different tasks and portfolio activities which will help you to show your knowledge and understanding of early years care and education at NVQ/SVQ Level 2.

The first eight units form the core of NVQ Level 2 Early Years Care and Education. These are called:

C1   Support Children's Physical Development Needs
C4   Support Children's Social and Emotional Development
C8   Implement Planned Activities for Sensory and Intellectual Development
C9   Implement Planned Activities for the Development of Language and
       Communication Skills
E1   Maintain an Attractive, Stimulating and Reassuring Environment for Children
E2   Maintain the Safety and Security of Children
M3   Contribute to the Achievement of Organisational Requirements
P1   Relate to Parents

The remaining five units in the workbook provide tasks which cover the optional units.

C12   Feed babies
C13   Provide for Babies' Physical Development Needs
M1   Monitor, Store and Prepare Materials and Equipment
P9   Work with Parents in a Group
CU10   Contribute to the Effectiveness of Work Teams

REMEMBER
If you are using the materials in this workbook for assessment purposes for the NVQ/SVQ Level 2, it is important to discuss your work with your assessor as he/she may require further evidence of your understanding of a unit. You may also find that some tasks overlap. It is not necessary to repeat the work.

Portfolio activities

As you progress through the workbook you will be asked to complete portfolio activities. These are practical tasks which should relate to your work setting, if possible. The activities include observations of children, planning activities for children, designing posters, preparing booklets or leaflets to explain information to staff and/or parents.

It is important that you store your portfolio activities in a safe place as you may want to have the materials assessed for the NVQ/SVQ in Early Years Care and Education. You may find it helpful to use an A4 file for this. If you do, then these guidelines may be of value to you:

- Write your name and address clearly at the beginning of the file. (This may be invaluable if you leave your file on the bus!)
- If you are working with young children, describe your place of work and the age range of the children you are working with. Do not name the work setting or the staff with whom you work or the name of the child or family. It is important to retain confidentiality at all times.
- Begin a contents page. This can be very useful when trying to find specific activities.
- Use dividers to separate individual units.
- Number the pages of your file.
- Begin to compile a references and bibliography section. It is always important to note the title, author, date of publication and publisher of any books or articles you have referred to as you have worked on your answers. However, do not be tempted to leave it until you have finished the workbook. You will never be able to find the information and it will become an extremely boring and time-consuming task.

Recording your portfolio activities

When writing up your portfolio activities you should provide as much information as possible. It should include:

- The criteria number, eg C8.1.
- The aim of the activity, eg To observe the rest and sleep patterns of a child.
- Details of preparation and resources required.
- The starting and finishing time of the observation, if appropriate.
- The number of adults and children present during the activity.
- The first names of the child/children or other identification, eg first letter of the child's name.
- A brief description of the child/children including details of age, gender and other relevant information.
- Details on how effective the activity/observation was.
- How the information gained helps with future work with children and families.

Progress Checklist

Throughout the workbook you will find progress grids. When you have completed a question/portfolio activity you can tick the relevant box on the progress grid. This will help you to plan your work and monitor your progress. You should aim to provide activities and/or observations for as wide an age range of children as possible.

USEFUL BOOKS

Beaver, M. and Brewster, J. et al (1994) *Babies and Young Children Book 1 Development 0–7 years.* Cheltenham: Stanley Thornes.

Bee, H. (1993) *The Developing Child* 5th Edition. London: MacMillan.

Bruce, T. (1996) *Helping Children to Play.* London: Hodder and Stoughton.

Bruce, T. and Meggitt, C. (1999) *Child Care and Education.* 2nd Edition. London: Hodder & Stoughton.

Dare, A. and P. O'Donovan (1994). *A Practical Guide to Working with Babies.* Cheltenham: Stanley Thornes.

Davies, M. (1995) *Helping Children to Learn Through a Movement Perspective.* London: Hodder & Stoughton.

Davenport, G. (1994) *An Introduction to Child Development.* London: Unwin Hyman.

Lindon, J. and Lindon, L. (1993) *Caring for the Under 8's.* London: MacMillan.

Malik, H. (1998) *Practical Guide to Equal Opportunities.* Cheltenham: Stanley Thornes.

Minet, P. (1994) *Child Care and Development.* London: John Murray.

O'Hagan, M. (1997) *Geraghty's Caring for Children.* 3rd Edition. London: Balliere Tindall.

O'Hagan, M. and Smith, M. (1993) *Special Issues in Child Care.* London: Balliere Tindall.

Roberts, R. (1995) *Self Esteem and Successful Early Learning.* London: Hodder & Stoughton.

What should I do now?

Follow the seven steps given below to help you complete the workbook.

Step 1 READ

Step 2   DISCUSS

Step 3   CHOOSE

Step 4   RESEARCH

Step 5   OBSERVE

Step 6   RECORD

Step 7   ASSESSMENT

Step 1 Choose the unit that you would like to start with. It may be a topic that you are particularly interested in or one that you are familiar with. Read through the unit carefully before you begin to fill in the answers. Do not be tempted to start answering questions straight away as you may give yourself a lot of additional work.

Step 2 If you have a mentor or tutor, discuss the content of the unit with him/her. Your mentor or tutor will help you to plan a programme of work. If you do not have a mentor or tutor it may be useful to complete a programme of work such as the one started on p. 4 for Unit C2. A separate one would need to be completed for each unit.

Step 3 Choose an appropriate section to start with. You do not have to start at the beginning of every section.

Step 4 Begin to gather information. This will mean visiting the library, reading appropriate articles in magazines and books, and visiting local government offices etc.

Step 5 Observe and record any appropriate information. You may want to take photographs of the work you are doing to include in your portfolio. If you do take photographs, remember to ask permission.

Step 6 When you feel you have gathered all the necessary information and you understand the work, you should then complete the relevant section in the unit. Additional work should be clearly named and attached to your unit.

Step 7 When you have finished the unit, read over your work again and make sure that you have included all the relevant information. When you are satisfied with your work, you are then ready to go on to the next unit.

Example programme of work

This is the sort of programme of work you should aim to complete for each unit. These notes will help you to see at a glance what needs to be done for each criteria, so helping you to cover all aspects effectively without wasting time or doubling up on information.

Unit	Number	Notes
C1	*2*	Visit your local library for information on the nutritional value of foods. Local health stores may have leaflets.

Mandatory Unit CSC97EY – C1

SUPPORT CHILDREN'S PHYSICAL DEVELOPMENT NEEDS

DESCRIPTIONS OF KNOWLEDGE, UNDERSTANDING AND SKILLS

Development		Evidence method	Evidence reference
1	basic knowledge of children's physical development and how it relates to other aspects of their development C1.1.2, 5; C1.2.1, 3, 4; C1.3.1, 6; C1.4.2		
2	basic dietary requirements for good health C1.2.1		
3	importance of children adhering to diets derived from culture, wish or belief, and from food allergies C1.2.1		
4	the effects of illness on the appetite and how this affects learning, behaviour and social interaction C1.2.6		
5	the general role of exercise in promoting physical growth and development C1.3.6		
6	the relationship between level of child's development and physical abilities and appropriate exercise C1.3.1, 6		
7	importance of rest, sleep and quiet periods as part of daily routine C1.4.2, 3		

Curriculum Practice		Evidence method	Evidence reference
8	the role adults play in helping children to become more self-reliant whilst still ensuring their safety C1.1.2		
9	the value of social action at mealtimes C1.2.6		

Mandatory Unit CSC97EY – C1

SUPPORT CHILDREN'S PHYSICAL DEVELOPMENT NEEDS

10	the role of physical achievement in developing self confidence C1.3.8		
11	indicators of stereotypical approaches to exercise and how to provide non-stereotypical exercise and play C1.3.8		
12	methods of providing for different types of exercise and physical activity C1.3.6, 7		
13	general knowledge of how to recognise signs of possible infection, injury or abuse C1.1.6		

Equipment, Materials, Environment		Evidence method	Evidence reference
14	basic knowledge of health, safety and hygiene in the care of children C1.1.3, 7, 9, 10; C1.2.2, 4, 7, 8; C1.3.12, 13; C1.4.5, 6		
15	basic knowledge of the health and safety policy and procedures of the setting C1.1.10; C1.2.7, 8; C1.3.5, 10, 13; C1.4.6		
16	the importance of adequate supervision for children during physical exercise C1.3.8		
17	how to undertake simple adaptations to equipment to suit children's needs and safety requirements C1.3.3, 5, 7		
18	types of constraints of the setting that might affect use of outdoor play C1.3.9		
19	how to make the most effective use of space and equipment C1.3.3, 7; C4.4.1		

Mandatory Unit CSC97EY – C1

SUPPORT CHILDREN'S PHYSICAL DEVELOPMENT NEEDS

Relationships	Evidence method	Evidence reference
20 the importance of children following the cultural practices of their families, and of respecting the practices of others C1.1.8; C1.2.1, 5, 6; C1.3.2, 8		
21 routines, including toileting, rest and sleep match those of home C1.4.3		

Grid C1

Please tick box when activity is complete:
P = Portfolio Activity

DEVELOPMENT	1	2	3
	P	**P**	
	4	5	6
			P
	7		

CURRICULUM PRACTICE	8	9	10
	11	12	13
		P	

EQUIPMENT, MATERIALS, ENVIRONMENT	14	15	16
		P	
	17	18	19
	P		**P**

RELATIONSHIPS	20	21	
		P	

MANDATORY UNIT

C1 SUPPORT CHILDREN'S PHYSICAL DEVELOPMENT NEEDS

Description of knowledge, understanding and skills

DEVELOPMENT

1   ***Portfolio Activity***

Design a booklet for parents which explains the physical development of a young child aged 6 weeks to 7 years 11 months. It should also show how it relates to other aspects of their development.

2   ***Portfolio Activity***

(a) What should a child's diet contain in order to ensure good health?

(b) Plan a balanced meal for a three year old child.

3   When planning meals for young children, why is it important to take account of the child's

(a) culture

....

....

(b) belief

....

....

(c) food allergy?

....

....

4 How does illness affect the child's:

(a) appetite

....

....

(b) learning

....

....

(c) behaviour

....

....

(d) social interaction

....

....

5 Describe how exercise can promote the physical growth and development of:

(a) a pre-school child

....

....

(b) a school child

....

....

6&12   *Portfolio Activity*

Plan and implement ONE activity which will promote the physical development of a child. Explain why you chose the activity and what the child gained from it.

7   Why is it important for children to have time to rest or have a quiet time during the day?

....

....

....

....

....

....

....

....

....

....

....

....

....

....

....

....

....

CURRICULUM PRACTICE

8   *(a)* A three year old child is playing on the climbing frame for the first time. How can the adult encourage the child whilst still ensuring that he/she is safe?

....

....

(b) A six-year-old child has decided to bake some cakes. How can the adult encourage the child whilst still ensuring that he/she is safe?

....

....

9   What is the value of social action at mealtimes?

....

....

....

....

10   Describe how a child's self confidence can be developed through physical exercise.

....

....

....

....

11   Describe how the child care and education worker can promote non-stereotypical exercise and play.

....

....

12   You have answered this as part of number 6.

13   List THREE signs for EACH of the following:

(a) possible infection

....

....

....

(b) injury

....

....

....

(c) abuse

....

....

....

14   How can the child care and education worker ensure the health and safety of the child in his/her care? Give FIVE examples for each

(a) indoor environment

....

....

....

....

....

(b) outdoor environment

....

....

....

....

....

Design a poster or leaflet which explains how to ensure a hygienic environment for young children to work in.

15 *Portfolio Activity*

Collect information which explains the health and safety regulations of the work setting.

16 Why is it important to supervise children during physical exercise?

....

....

....

....

....

17 *Portfolio Activity*

Describe how the work setting makes changes to the equipment and space to meet the children's physical needs while ensuring safety.

18 What could prevent children experiencing outdoor play at the work setting? Give FIVE examples.

....

....

....

....

....

19 *Portfolio Activity*

Draw a plan of a nursery for children aged between 3 and 5 years.
The plan should show:

(a) the equipment that you are providing
(b) where the equipment will be placed

RELATIONSHIPS

20   *(a)* Why is it important that children follow the cultural practices of their families?

....

....

....

....

....

....

....

....

(b) Why is it important to respect the cultural practices of others?

....

....

....

....

....

....

....

21   *Portfolio Activity*

Plan a daily routine for a child in your care. It should include:

(a) toileting
(b) rest and sleep

Why is it important to discuss the routine with the parent before implementing it?

C4 – Mandatory Unit CSC97EY

SUPPORT CHILDREN'S SOCIAL AND EMOTIONAL DEVELOPMENT

DESCRIPTIONS OF KNOWLEDGE, UNDERSTANDING AND SKILLS

Development	Evidence method	Evidence reference
1 basic knowledge of children's social and emotional development and how this relates to other aspects of their development C4.2.2; C4.4.2; C4.5.1		
2 awareness of individual children's needs in relation to social and emotional development, change and separation and that these may vary with individuals C4.1.4, 5; C4.2.2		
3 how children are affected by changes and how they differ in the time taken to adjust to the care/education setting and the different types and levels of support required C4.1.5, 6, 7		
4 own role in the setting, the roles of other workers and the liaison with other professional groups including boundaries of confidentiality C4.4.6; C4.5.7, 8		
5 the importance of, and methods of, welcoming children and recognising their individual needs C4.1.1, 2		
6 recognition of racist, sexist, abusive and anti-social behaviour the effects this has on children's social and emotional development and how to challenge such behaviour C4.2.4, 5, 7		
7 the development of self-reliance and self-esteem as a gradual process and how this is affected by maturation and the development of communication skills in children C4.3.1, 2, 4, 5, 7		
8 the importance for the child's social and emotional development of learning to recognise, name and deal with their feelings and the feelings of others C4.4.3, 5		

C4 – Mandatory Unit CSC97EY

SUPPORT CHILDREN'S SOCIAL AND EMOTIONAL DEVELOPMENT

9	how to recognise signs of distress in a child C4.4.4		
10	the factors and circumstances which may encourage or provoke children to display difficult and negative behaviour C4.5.4		
11	the powerful nature of feelings in young children and appropriate expectations of control C4.4.1, 2, 3, 4		

Curriculum Practice		Evidence method	Evidence reference
12	how to provide play activities and strategies to promote self-reliance and self-esteem and how they may be adjusted to take account of children from various cultural backgrounds, genders and with special needs C4.2.1, 5, 6; C4.3.3, 4, 5, 7, 8		
13	a range of activities, routines and strategies which encourage respect for the individual child and understand the rationale behind these C4.3.3, 4		
14	the importance of boundary setting and consistency of application by significant adults C4.5.3, 5		
15	strategies for encouraging the expression of positive and negative feelings in words and actions where appropriate C4.4.4, 6		
16	the rationale behind a calm and reassuring manner when dealing with children who are emotionally upset, including awareness of safety and minimum disruption to other children C4.4.1, 3, 4		

C4 – Mandatory Unit CSC97EY

SUPPORT CHILDREN'S SOCIAL AND EMOTIONAL DEVELOPMENT

17	the reason for the settling in strategies of the care/education setting and the need for flexibility C4.1.2, 3		
18	techniques of physical and non physical control C4.5.6		

Equipment, Materials, Environment	Evidence method	Evidence reference
19 assessment of materials and equipment which help towards the social and emotional development of children C4.2.1, 6		
20 the behaviour management policy of the setting C4.5.2, 3, 4, 5, 6		

Relationships	Evidence method	Evidence reference
21 variations in cultural expectations about children's independence and inter-dependence C4.3.9		
22 the importance of preparing children and adults in the new setting to receive newcomers C4.1.1		
23 the role of the adult in the resolution of conflict situations among children and the rationale behind it C4.2.3, 4, 5		
24 the importance of supporting children who are the object of abuse C4.2.7		

C4 – Mandatory Unit CSC97EY

SUPPORT CHILDREN'S SOCIAL AND EMOTIONAL DEVELOPMENT

25	the importance of communication with and knowing how to listen and encourage interaction between children, adults and children C4.3.1		
26	when to praise a child for his/her efforts and the rationale behind positive reinforcement for effort C4.3.6, 7		
27	a range of strategies to encourage negotiation with children, know their possible outcomes and understand the need for flexibility in their application C4.3.7, 8		

Grid C4

Please tick box when activity is complete:
P = Portfolio Activity

DEVELOPMENT	1	2	3
	P		
	4	5	6
	P	**P**	
	7	8	9
	10	11	

CURRICULUM PRACTICE	12	13	14
	P	**P**	
	15	16	17
			P
	18		

EQUIPMENT, MATERIALS, ENVIRONMENT	19	20	
		P	

RELATIONSHIPS	21	22	23
	24	25	26
	27		
	P		

C4 SUPPORT CHILDREN'S SOCIAL AND EMOTIONAL DEVELOPMENT

Description of knowledge, understanding and skills

DEVELOPMENT

1   ***Portfolio Activity***

Design a booklet for parents which explains the social and emotional development of a young child aged 6 weeks to 7 years 11 months. It should also show how it relates to other aspects of their development.

2   Describe the needs of a child who has started in a new setting.

....

....

....

....

....

....

....

....

....

3   How might children be affected by the following changes in their lives:

(a) moving house

....

....

....

(b) marital breakdown

....

....

....

(c) new baby?

....

....

....

How can the child care and education worker support the child through EACH of these changes?

....

....

....

....

....

 4   ***Portfolio Activity***
Describe:

(a) your own role in the work setting;
(b) the role of the other workers in the setting;
(c) how the work setting liaises with other professional;
(d) the policies of the work setting on confidentiality.

5   *Portfolio Activity*

Describe how you would welcome the child/children to the work setting at the start of the day. Explain why it is important to do this.

6   How can the following types of behaviour affect a child's social and emotional behaviour? For EACH type of behaviour suggest ways in which the carer can promote positive attitudes.

(a) racist behaviour

....

....

....

....

(b) sexist behaviour

....

....

....

....

(c) abusive behaviour

....

....

....

....

(d) anti-social behaviour

....

....

....

....

7   Describe the way in which a child develops self-reliance and self-esteem.
     Explain how it is affected by maturation and the development of
     communication skills.

     ....

     ....

     ....

     ....

     ....

     ....

8   Why is it important for a child to learn to recognise and deal with his/her
     feelings?

     ....

     ....

     ....

     ....

     ....

     ....

9   Name THREE signs of distress in a child other than crying.

     ....

     ....

     ....

     ....

     ....

     ....

10 List THREE factors and/or circumstances which may encourage a child to behave in an unacceptable way.

(a)

....

....

....

(b)

....

....

....

(c)

....

....

....

11 A two year-old child is having a temper tantrum in a shop. Is this unusual behaviour for a child? Give reasons for your answer.

....

....

....

....

....

....

....

....

CURRICULUM PRACTICE

12&13   *Portfolio Activity*

Plan and implement THREE activities which will promote the self esteem and self respect of a child. Give reasons for your choice of activity.

(a) Describe how the first activity may be changed to take account of children from various cultural backgrounds.

(b) Describe how the second activity may be changed to take account of a child of the opposite gender.

(c) Describe how the third activity may be changed to take account of a child with special needs.

14   Why is it important for all adults in the work setting to use the same rules of behaviour when working with children?

....

....

....

....

....

....

15   Describe how the child care and education worker can encourage a child to show his/her positive AND negative feelings.

....

....

....

....

....

....

....

16   Why is it important for the child care and education worker to have a quiet and calm manner when working with a distressed child?

....

....

....

....

....

....

....

....

17   *Portfolio Activity*

Design a programme which may be used to help a child AND the parent become familiar with a new setting. Give reasons for the content of the programme and explain the value of it.

18   Describe ONE method of physical control and ONE method of non-physical control which could be used by the child care and education worker.

....

....

....

....

....

....

....

....

EQUIPMENT, MATERIALS, ENVIRONMENT

19   Complete the table below. THREE pieces of equipment and/or materials have been given to you. You will need to add THREE more pieces of equipment or materials.

Equipment/Materials	Effectiveness of equipment/materials in promoting social and emotional development
Dolls	
Water	
Clay	

20   ***Portfolio Activity***

Provide or write a behaviour management policy for your work setting.

RELATIONSHIPS

21   Choose TWO different cultures. Describe the expectations that EACH culture has about the child's independence and inter-dependence.

....

....

....

....

....

22   Why is it important to tell the children and staff in the work setting that a new child is starting?

....

....

....

....

....

23   A small group of three-year-old children are playing in the home area. Two of the children begin to argue as they both want the same doll. They are each holding the doll and trying to pull it towards them. How can the adult manage this situation? Give reasons for your answer.

....

....

....

....

....

24   A five-year-old child is being bullied by other children in the school playground. Why is it important for the adult to support the child and what action may be taken?

....

....

....

....

....

....

....

....

25   Why is it important to listen to children?

Describe the advice you would give to an inexperienced member of staff on how to encourage children to talk with each other and to adults.

....

....

....

....

....

....

....

....

26   What is meant by positive reinforcement and why should a child care and education worker use positive reinforcement when working with a child?

....

....

....

....

....

....

....

....

....

27   *Portfolio Activity*

Describe situations where you have negotiated with a child in order to:

(a) achieve a task
(b) resolve a dilemma

Mandatory Unit CSC97EY – C8

IMPLEMENT PLANNED ACTIVITIES FOR SENSORY AND INTELLECTUAL DEVELOPMENT

DESCRIPTIONS OF KNOWLEDGE, UNDERSTANDING AND SKILLS

Development		Evidence method	Evidence reference
1	basic knowledge of sensory and intellectual development C8.1.1; C8.2.2, 5, 7, 10; C8.4.1, 4		
2	the sequence of development of children's play with particular reference to parallel play, co-operative play, turn-taking, sharing and the ability to cope with rules C8.2.1, 2, 6, 9		
3	the role of different types of play in children's development C8.1.1; C8.2.1, 2, 3, 5, 7, 10; C8.3.10		
4	the effects of competitive games and losing on children's behaviour and self esteem C8.2.2, 5, 10		
5	demands of different cooking processes and recipes in relation to children of different ages and levels of development C8.3.1, 2, 8, 9		
6	why and how examination and sensory exploration of objects of interest can be used to promote children's development C8.5.1, 2, 3, 4, 5, 6, 7, 8, 9		

Curriculum Practice		Evidence method	Evidence reference
7	the role of an overall curriculum plan in relation to selection, layout and presentation of materials and equipment for children's activities all C8.		
8	the activities, equipment and materials involved in creative play and their properties C8.1.1, 2, 3, 4		

Mandatory Unit CSC97EY – C8

IMPLEMENT PLANNED ACTIVITIES FOR SENSORY AND INTELLECTUAL DEVELOPMENT

9	general principles of healthy eating and "healthy eating" recipes C8.3.11		
10	a variety of recipes suitable for making with children including recipes from various cultures C8.3.1, 2, 8		
11	how to support and encourage children in their activities without disrupting their play or detracting from their overall control/self-reliance C8.4.6		
12	the differences between fine and gross motor play C8.4.4		
13	how to build on children's natural curiosity and how not to stifle it C8.5.5, 7		
14	how to extend the children's understanding of cultures other than their own through thematic approaches C8.5.2		
15	how to encourage children to treat cultural artefacts with respect C8.5.2		
16	how to adapt cooking activities to enable the participation of children with special needs C8.3.3, 4, 9		
17	hygiene requirements and health and safety procedures of the setting in relation to food preparation, eating and storage C8.3.2, 4, 5, 6, 7		
18	how to handle children who are disruptive and unco-operative and those who won't want to join in C8.2.3, 8, 9		

Mandatory Unit CSC97EY – C8

IMPLEMENT PLANNED ACTIVITIES FOR SENSORY AND INTELLECTUAL DEVELOPMENT

Equipment, Materials, Environment	Evidence method	Evidence reference
19 the potential hazards and the safety measures associated with natural and other materials C8.1.2, 3, 4, 5		
20 a range of ways to set out and present materials attractively C8.1.1, 2, 3, 6 C8.4.3, 4, 5, 6; C8.5.6		
21 health and safety requirements of the setting C8.1.2, 3, 5, 7, 8; C8.4.2, 3, 5, 7, 8, 9, 10		
22 how to devise and improvise children's games C8.2.1, 2, 5, 7, 10		
23 why specific games and activities have been selected C8.2.1, 2, 3, 4, 5		
24 selection of special equipment and how to adapt existing equipment C8.2.1, 2, 3, 5, 7, 10		
25 games and equipment to enable the participation of children with special needs C8.4.1		
26 the potential effect of traditional games in gender stereotyping and how to counteract this C8.2.1, 3, 10		
27 the range of themes, objects and materials that reflect the cultural background of the children and why and how these can be used to extend the children's understanding of other cultures C8.5.1, 2, 5		
28 how to enable children with sensory impairment to explore and examine objects effectively C8.5.7		

Grid C8

Please tick box when activity is complete:
P = Portfolio Activity

DEVELOPMENT	1	2	3
	P		
	4	5	6
		P	

CURRICULUM PRACTICE	7	8	9
	10	11	12
	P		
	13	14	15
		P	**P**
	16	17	18
	P	**P**	**P**

EQUIPMENT, MATERIALS, ENVIRONMENT	19	20	21
		P	
	22	23	24
	P	**P**	**P**
	25	26	27
	28		

MANDATORY UNIT

C8 IMPLEMENT PLANNED ACTIVITIES FOR SENSORY AND INTELLECTUAL DEVELOPMENT

Description of knowledge, understanding and skills

DEVELOPMENT

1 ***Portfolio Activity***

   Design a booklet for parents which explains the sensory and intellectual development of a young child aged 6 weeks to 7 years 11 months.

2 Place the following types of play in order, with number 1 being used by the youngest child.

   ☐ spectator/on-looking play   ☐ co-operative play

   ☐ parallel play   ☐ solitary

   ☐ play games with rules   ☐ associative

3 'My child always seems to be playing and never works'.
   Describe the role of play as part of the child's development.

4   When children play competitive games, what effect could losing have on:

(a) their behaviour

....

....

....

....

....

(b) their self esteem

....

....

....

....

....

5&16   *Portfolio Activity*

Plan and implement a cooking activity with a child or small group of children. The plan should include a detailed recipe. In your evaluation explain the difficulties the children had during the cooking process due to their level of development. Explain how cooking activities could be adapted to enable a child with special needs to participate.

6   How can children learn from handling interesting objects?

....

....

....

....

....

....

CURRICULUM PRACTICE

7   Why is it important to have an overall curriculum plan when deciding on the selection, layout and presentation of materials and equipment for children's activities? (NB Consider unexpected situations beyond your control.)

....

....

....

....

....

....

....

....

....

....

8   What activities, equipment and materials may be used to promote creative play?

Complete the table below.

Promoting Creative Play	
Activities	
Equipment	
Materials	

9   What should a child's diet contain in order to ensure good health? You may
have answered this question as part of C1 number 2.

....

....

....

....

....

....

....

....

10   *Portfolio Activity*

*Collect different recipes that may be used with children of different ages. There should be
recipes from different cultures and they should promote 'healthy eating'.*

11   How can the child care and education worker support a child during an
activity without disrupting the play?

....

....

....

....

....

....

....

....

12   Explain the difference between fine and gross motor play.

....

....

....

....

....

....

....

....

13   How can the adult encourage the child's curiosity?

....

....

....

....

....

....

....

....

14,15,27   *Portfolio Activity*

(a) *Choose a theme which reflects a culture that is different to the majority of children in the work setting. Plan a variety of different activities for the children.*

(b) *List FOUR different objects and/or materials from your theme that may be used to extend the children's understanding of other cultures.*

16   You may already have answered this question as part of (5).

17   *Portfolio Activity*

What are the health and safety procedures of your work setting in relation to:

(a) food preparation
(b) eating?

How would you store the following types of food:

(a) cooked chicken

....

....

(b) raw meat

....

....

(c) eggs

....

....

(d) bread

....

....

(e) vegetables

....

....

18   *Portfolio Activity*

Write a short description of your own personal effectiveness in encouraging children to participate when they did not want to AND how you dealt with children who were being disruptive.

EQUIPMENT, MATERIALS AND ENVIRONMENT

19   What safety considerations must be taken into account when working with
        natural and other materials?

....

....

....

....

....

....

....

....

....

....

....

....

....

....

....

....

....

20   **Portfolio Activity**

        Plan and implement different ways of setting out natural and other materials.

21   Describe the health and safety requirements of the work setting in relation to play materials.

....

....

....

....

....

....

....

....

....

....

....

....

....

22   *Portfolio Activity*

Make a child's table top game. Use it with an individual child or group of children and evaluate its effectiveness.

23&24   *Portfolio Activity*

Make a list of games and activities that you could use with the following groups of children:

(a) toddlers
(b) pre-school
(c) school aged

Include details of any special equipment you may need to use or how equipment may be adapted. Give reasons for your choice of game or activity.

25   Describe how the child care and education worker could adapt a game to
      ensure that a child with special needs could participate. Give examples.

      ....

      ....

      ....

      ....

      ....

      ....

      ....

      ....

      ....

26   List THREE games which promote gender stereotyping. For EACH game
      explain how they could be changed to prevent this.

      ....

      ....

      ....

      ....

      ....

      ....

      ....

      ....

27   You have answered this as part of number 14 and 15.

28   Describe how the child care and education worker can enable a child with a sensory impairment to explore and examine objects.

....

....

....

....

....

....

....

....

....

....

....

....

....

....

....

....

....

....

Mandatory Unit CSC97EY – C9

IMPLEMENT PLANNED ACTIVITIES FOR THE DEVELOPMENT OF LANGUAGE AND COMMUNICATION SKILLS

DESCRIPTIONS OF KNOWLEDGE, UNDERSTANDING AND SKILLS

Development	Evidence method	Evidence reference
1 basic knowledge of child development C9.1.1, 6; C9.2.1, 2, 3, 4; C9.3.1; C9.4.1		
2 a variety of common communication difficulties in children		
3 how child development knowledge relates to role play activities C9.3.1, 2		
4 the approximate attention-span of children of different ages and stages of development C9.1.2, 5, 6, 7; C9.5.1, 7		
5 how to adapt/design session including talking and listening C9.1.2, 6; C9.2.4, 7		
6 games and use of stories and rhymes to encourage participation of children with hearing or other sensory impairment C9.5.3, 4, 5		
7 the sequences of child development and the appropriateness of different types of books to the particular level C9.4.1, 3, 4, 5		
8 children's possible emotional responses to stories C9.5.9		

Mandatory Unit CSC97EY – C9

IMPLEMENT PLANNED ACTIVITIES FOR THE DEVELOPMENT OF LANGUAGE AND COMMUNICATION SKILLS

Curriculum Practice		Evidence method	Evidence reference
9	the role of the adult in supporting children's learning and development and the reasons why it is desirable to follow the child's lead and experiences C9.3.5; C9.5.3, 5, 6, 7, 8		
10	how to communicate with and listen to children C9.2.2, 3, 4, 5, 8		
11	the role of an overall curriculum plan in relation to selection, layout and presentation of materials and equipment for children's activities, and how to follow a theme through activities C9.2.1, 2; C9.3.3, 5; C9.4.1, 2, 5		
12	what role play is and what it may help to achieve in terms of a child's development, experience and creative potential C9.3.3		
13	how gender and cultural stereotypes may be expressed in words of traditional songs and rhymes and children's role play and how to counteract this C9.1.1, 2, 4; C9.3.5, 7		
14	appropriate songs, musical, talking and listening games and activities for children of different ages C9.1.1, 2, 6; C9.2.1, 2, 3, 4		
15	how literature and illustrative styles vary across culture and why it is important to show children's books in various languages and illustrative styles C9.5.2		
16	how to select and use visual aids to support story-telling C9.5.3		

Mandatory Unit CSC97EY – C9

IMPLEMENT PLANNED ACTIVITIES FOR THE DEVELOPMENT OF LANGUAGE AND COMMUNICATION SKILLS

Equipment, Materials, Environment		Evidence method	Evidence reference
17	types of songs which are or are not likely to work with groups of different size C9.1.1, 2		
18	how to set up areas and activities for role play C9.3.3, 5		
19	how to identify which equipment and materials reflect children's own cultural backgrounds and extend their knowledge of other cultural groupings C9.3.6, 7		
20	how to review books and stories in preparation for a story session, including the reasons why it is important to provide books with positive images and which are non-discriminatory C9.4.4; C9.5.1, 2		
21	where to locate appropriate books including use of libraries available to the child care/education setting C9.4.2, 3, 4		
22	health and safety requirements of the setting C9.3.2, 4; C9.4.8		

Grid C9

Please tick box when activity is complete:
P = Portfolio Activity

	1	2	3
DEVELOPMENT	**P**		
	4	5	6
	7	8	
	P	**P**	

	9	10	11
CURRICULUM PRACTICE			
	12	13	14
			P
	15	16	

	17	18	19
EQUIPMENT, MATERIALS, ENVIRONMENT	**P**	**P**	**P**
	20	21	22
	P		**P**

MANDATORY UNIT

C9 IMPLEMENT PLANNED ACTIVITIES FOR THE DEVELOPMENT OF LANGUAGE AND COMMUNICATION SKILLS

Description of knowledge, understanding and skills

DEVELOPMENT

1   ***Portfolio Activity***

Design a booklet for parents which explains the development of a young child aged 6 weeks to 7 years 11 months.

2   List THREE common communication difficulties that a child may experience.

....

....

....

3   How does child development relate to role play activities? Copy and complete the diagram below.

4   Look at the statements below, and number them according to the stages of attention span you would expect a child to progress through. (The earliest stage should be 1.)

☐ Concentrates on what is being done and blocks everything else out.

☐ Easily distracted.

☐ The child is able to leave the activity to listen to instructions and then go back to the activity.

☐ The child is able to leave the activity to listen to the instructions but he/she often needs help to return to the activity.

5   Describe how the child care and education worker may adapt a talking or listening game to allow a child with a particular need to participate.

....

....

....

....

....

....

6   Explain how the child care and education worker can ensure that a child with a sensory impairment can participate in:

(a) a game

....

....

(b) a story telling session.

....

....

7   *Portfolio Activity*

Provide evidence of a variety of types of books that have been used with different ages of children. They should include factual or information books and fiction books, picture books etc. Explain why they are appropriate for the chosen age group.

8   *Portfolio Activity*

Observe a story session and write an account of the emotional responses made by the children during the session.

CURRICULUM PRACTICE

9 *(a)* Describe the role of the adult in supporting children's learning and development.

....

....

(b) Why is it desirable to follow the child's lead and experiences?

....

....

10 Why is it important to listen to children?

....

....

....

Describe the advice you would give to an inexperienced member of staff on how to listen to young children.

....

....

Read the two questions below. Which question will encourage the child to talk? Give reasons for your choice.

(a) 'Would you like an apple or an orange?'

(b) 'What did you do yesterday?'

....

....

....

....

....

11   Why is it important to have an overall curriculum plan when deciding on the selection, layout and presentation of materials and equipment for children's activities? (You may already have answered this question in C8.7)

....

....

....

....

....

....

Choose a different theme for EACH of the ages shown below. Plan a range of activities that would be appropriate for the children.

(a) 1–3 years

A knowledge and understanding of different types of play should be shown in your plan.

(b) 3–4 years

A knowledge and understanding of the Desirable Outcomes should be shown in your plan.

12   What is 'role/pretend' play?

....

....

....

....

....

....

....

....

13   Using an example of your choice, show how you would change the words of a traditional song or rhyme to avoid stereotyping.

....

....

....

....

....

14&17   *Portfolio Activity*

Make a collection of songs, musical, talking and listening games and activities that may be used with children of different ages. Identify the songs that may be used with individual children, small groups of children and large groups of children.

15   Describe TWO differences that may be seen in books from different cultures.

....

....

....

....

....

Why is it important to show children books from different cultures?

....

....

....

....

....

....

16   List THREE visual aids that could be used when telling a story. Give reasons for your choice.

(a)

....

....

(b)

....

....

(c)

....

....

....

....

....

....

....

....

....

....

....

....

EQUIPMENT, MATERIALS AND ENVIRONMENT

17   This answer is part of 14.

18&19   *Portfolio Activity*

Plan a theme which helps to develop the role play of a child. Set up an area or an activity linked to the theme. The equipment/materials should reflect the child's cultural background. Describe how effective the activity/area was.

19   This answer is part of 18.

20   *Portfolio Activity*

Design a checklist which you could use to review books and stories in preparation for a story session. Review FIVE books in your checklist.

Why is it important to provide books with positive images and which are non-discriminatory?

....

....

....

....

....

....

....

....

....

....

....

21   Where can the child care and education worker find books that would be appropriate for children. Give THREE examples.

(a)

....

....

....

(b)

....

....

....

(c)

....

....

....

22   ***Portfolio Activity***
Collect information which explains the health and safety regulations of the work setting.
You may have answered this as part of C1 number 15.

Mandatory Unit CSC97EY – E1

MAINTAIN AN ATTRACTIVE, STIMULATING AND REASSURING ENVIRONMENT FOR CHILDREN

DESCRIPTIONS OF KNOWLEDGE, UNDERSTANDING AND SKILLS

Development		Evidence method	Evidence reference
1	how to predict and recognise common stages of anxiety or fear amongst children and what these are likely to be E.1.1.2, 7; E.1.3.1, 2, 3		
2	the effect of separation from their main carer on children's behaviour E.1.3.1, 2, 3, 4, 6		

Curriculum Practice		Evidence method	Evidence reference
3	how the physical layout helps children to learn about and have control over their activities E.1.1.3, 6, 7		
4	how the physical layout and activities meet children's physical needs E.1.1.2, 7		
5	responsibility of adults to enable children to explore their environment in safety and security E.1.1.1, 2, 6, 7		
6	ways children should be encouraged to participate in decision making and taking responsibility for their actions E.1.1.6		
7	why children need to feel secure and the effect on their confidence and abilities when their feelings of security are increased or decreased E.1.1.2		
8	methods of reassurance and dealing with anxiety or fears including comfort objects E.1.3.4, 5		

Mandatory Unit CSC97EY – E1

MAINTAIN AN ATTRACTIVE, STIMULATING AND REASSURING ENVIRONMENT FOR CHILDREN

9	the importance of displaying positive images of people who are often stereotyped or discriminated against on grounds of gender, racial origin, cultural background or disability E.1.1.6; E.1.2.3; E.1.3.6		

Equipment, Materials, Environment		Evidence method	Evidence reference
10	reasons why the care/education environment should reflect the home environment E.1.3.4, 5, 6		
11	how to lay out furniture to encourage communication in pairs, and in group activities E.1.1.3, 6, 7		
12	presentation of equipment and resources that can encourage/discourage different kinds of activities including individual and group work E.1.1.3, 7		
13	what modifications to the building and layout would cater for children with special needs E.1.1.2, 3, 6, 7		
14	the health and safety requirements for heating, lighting and access to the setting of any inspecting authority E.1.1.4, 5, 6		
15	how to display materials and children's creative work attractively to enable children and adults to discuss the content E.1.2.1, 2, 4, 5, 8, 9		
16	how to care for plants and other natural materials within the setting E.1.2.5		
17	displays, equipment and materials, include familiar items from children's homes especially kitchen and washing equipment, furnishings and fabrics, typical of a range of cultural, economic and social backgrounds E.1.2.3; E1.3.5, 6		

Grid E1

Please tick box when activity is complete:
P = Portfolio Activity

DEVELOPMENT	1	2	
	P		

	3	4	5
CURRICULUM PRACTICE			
	6	7	8
	9		

	10	11	12
EQUIPMENT, MATERIALS, ENVIRONMENT	13	14	15
	16	17	

E1 Maintain an Attractive, Stimulating and Reassuring Environment for Children

Description of knowledge, understanding and skills

DEVELOPMENT

1   List TWO different common sources of anxiety or fear for EACH of the following stages of development:

   (a) babies

   ....
   ....
   ....
   ....

   (b) toddlers

   ....
   ....
   ....
   ....

   (c) pre-school

   ....
   ....
   ....
   ....

2   When moving to a new setting, what effect can the separation from the main carer have on the child's behaviour?

....

....

....

....

....

....

....

....

....

....

....

....

....

....

....

....

....

....

CURRICULUM PRACTICE

3&4   How does the physical layout of the work setting:

(a) help the child to learn about and have control over their activities?

....

....

....

(b) meet the child's needs?

....

....

....

5   Why is it the responsibility of the adult to ensure that the child can explore their environment in safety and security?

....

....

....

6   Give THREE ways in which the child could participate in decision making within the work setting.

(a)

....

....

(b)

....

....

(c)

....

....

How can a child be encouraged to take responsibility for his/her own actions?

....

....

....

....

....

....

7 Why does a child need to be able to explore his/her environment in safety and security?

....

....

....

....

....

....

8 How can the child care and education worker help a child deal with a fear that he/she may have? Give TWO examples. State the type of fear and age of the child.

....

....

....

....

....

....

9   Why is it important to display positive images of people who are often stereotyped or discriminated against?

....

....

....

....

....

....

....

....

....

....

....

....

....

....

....

....

....

....

....

EQUIPMENT, MATERIALS, ENVIRONMENT

10   Why is it important that the care/education environment reflects the home environment?

....

....

11   Describe how the furniture in the work setting may be laid out to encourage communication:

(a) in pairs

....

....

....

....

(b) in group activities

....

....

....

....

12   How can the presentation of equipment and resources in the work setting:

(a) encourage the participation of individual children and groups of children in different types of activities

....

....

(b) discourage the participation of individual children and groups of children in different types of activities

....

....

13   *Portfolio Activity*

Draw a plan of your work setting. Indicate how the building and layout caters for or could cater for children with special needs.

14   Describe the health and safety requirements for the work setting with regard to:

(a) heating

....

....

....

(b) lighting

....

....

....

(c) access for inspecting authorities.

....

....

....

15 &17   *Portfolio Activity*

Provide evidence in your portfolio of TWO displays that you have arranged in the work setting. Use TWO different display techniques. Describe:

(a) the equipment and materials that were used. These should include familiar items from children's homes and reflect a range of cultural, economic and social backgrounds

(b) how you arranged the materials in order to attract the children's attention

(c) a conversation that took place between an adult and a child or group of children about the display.

16   *Portfolio Activity*

Design a series of cards which will explain to the children how to care for plants and other natural materials in the work setting. The cards may or may not have words on them.

17   This answer is part of 15.

E2 – Mandatory Unit CSC97EY

MAINTAIN THE SAFETY AND SECURITY OF CHILDREN

DESCRIPTIONS OF KNOWLEDGE, UNDERSTANDING AND SKILLS

Development		Evidence method	Evidence reference
1	basic knowledge of children's development and importance of taking account of this when considering safety arrangements E.2.2.2, 3, 4, 5, 7		
2	how to recognise and cope with children's emotional reaction to accidents and emergencies E.2.4.4, 6		
3	the physical and emotional signs of physical abuse, emotional abuse, neglect and sexual abuse including bruises on a range of skin tomes E.2.5.1, 2, 3, 4		
4	the significance of negative changes in children's behaviour and the importance of observing, recording and reporting this E.2.5.2		
5	the parts of the body where bruises are not usually caused by accidents E.2.5.1, 3, 4		
6	basic knowledge of child development and how outings can enhance children's learning E.2.6.1, 6		
7	a range of suitable outings for children of different ages E.2.6.1		

Equipment, Materials, Environment		Evidence method	Evidence reference
8	basic knowledge of health, safety and hygiene in the care of young children, including outings E.2.1., 2, 7; E.2.6.10		

E2 – Mandatory Unit CSC97EY

MAINTAIN THE SAFETY AND SECURITY OF CHILDREN

9	the procedures for identifying, minimising, reporting and correcting any safety hazards, indoors and outdoors, as quickly as possible in a manner which does not undermine the confidence of children E.2.1.6, 8		
10	why and how to carry out routine safety checks on premises and equipment E.2.1.3, 4, 5, 6, 7, 8, 9, 10		
11	the importance of adhering to manufacturers recommendations and relevant safety standards when using equipment E.2.1.3, 4		
12	the registration requirements for adult/child ratios of the setting and the importance of adhering to these E.2.2.1, 7		
13	the importance of policies and procedures for collection of children taking account of any special circumstances and maintaining records to enable parents to be contacted quickly if necessary E.2.2.8; E.2.3.1, 3		
14	routine emergency procedures and how to respond promptly in a calm and reassuring way appropriate to such situations E.2.3.4; E.2.4.3, 4, 6		
15	health and safety requirements of the setting and the importance of ensuring these are displayed and communicated to other adults in the setting all pcs – E.2.1; E.2.3; E.2.2.3, 5		
16	individual responsibilities in relation to safety including the settings requirements for recording accidents and emergencies all pcs – E.2.3; E.2.4.7		

E2 – Mandatory Unit CSC97EY

MAINTAIN THE SAFETY AND SECURITY OF CHILDREN

17	the policies and procedures of the setting for handling and disposing of body fluids and waste material particularly in light of AIDS/HIV virus and hepatitis etc. E.2.4.5		
18	basic first aid required in an emergency and how to apply it E.2.4.3		
19	knowledge of the required contents of first aid box, who should replenish it and why the contents need regular checking E.2.4.1, 2		
20	how to plan and prepare for an outing, with regard to safety, transport requirements, appropriate clothing, food and equipment E.2.6.5, 6, 7		
21	the regulations including insurance cover regarding the safe transportation of children in private cars E.2.6.8		
22	the importance of keeping a list of children on outings and why it should be checked at regular intervals E.2.6.4		

Relationships		Evidence method	Evidence reference
23	the reasons why and the types of adult anxiety/inappropriate reactions to events that can be transmitted to children; and how over-protection can prevent a child from developing self-confidence E.2.2.2, 3		
24	how to convey information to parents without causing undue alarm E.2.4.8		

E2 – Mandatory Unit CSC97EY

MAINTAIN THE SAFETY AND SECURITY OF CHILDREN

25	the importance of adhering to regulations laid down in the setting with regard to suspected child abuse and the boundaries of work roles regarding child abuse E.2.5.1, 2, 3, 5		
26	the importance of informing line manager of explanations of injuries given by parent/carer E.2.5.3, 5		
27	how to observe children while carrying out care routines for signs of injuries and abrasions and how and when these are reported E.2.5.1		
28	the importance of involving parents/carers from the early stages of enquiries within the policies of the setting E.2.5.4, 5		
29	the necessity of obtaining the permission of line manager before taking children off the premises and when it is appropriate to obtain parental permission E.2.6.2		

Grid E2

Please tick box when activity is complete:
P = Portfolio Activity

	1	2	3
DEVELOPMENT	P		
	4	5	6
	7		

	8	9	10
EQUIPMENT, MATERIALS, ENVIRONMENT	P	P	P
	11	12	13
		P	P
	14	15	16
		P	P
	17	18	19
	P	P	
	20	21	22
	P		

	23	24	25
RELATIONSHIPS			
	26	27	28
	29		

MANDATORY UNIT

E2 MAINTAIN THE SAFETY AND SECURITY OF CHILDREN

Description of knowledge, understanding and skills

DEVELOPMENT

1   ***Portfolio Activity***

Design a booklet for parents which explains the development of a young child aged 6 weeks to 7 years 11 months. You may have answered this question as part of C9 number 1.

Explain why it is important to use your knowledge of child development when considering the safety arrangements of the work setting.

2   A child can be emotionally upset if he/she is involved in an accident or emergency.

(a) What signs may indicate that the child is upset? Give THREE examples.

....

....

....

(b) How should the child care and education worker respond to the child?

....

....

....

3   List THREE different physical and emotional signs for EACH form of abuse:

(a) physical abuse

....

....

....

(b) emotional abuse

....

....

....

(c) neglect

....

....

....

(d) sexual abuse

....

....

....

How would you recognise bruising on different skin tones?

....

....

....

....

....

4   Why is it important to observe, record and report unusual changes in a child's behaviour?

....

....

....

....

....

....

....

5   Describe the parts of the body where bruises are not usually caused by accidents.

....

....

....

....

....

....

....

6&7   Choose a different location which may be used for an outing for EACH of the following age groups:

(a) 1 to 4 years

....

(b) 4 to 7 years 11 months.

....

Explain how EACH outing may enhance the children's learning.

(a)

....

....

....

....

....

....

....

....

....

(b)

....

....

....

....

....

....

....

....

....

....

EQUIPMENT, MATERIALS, ENVIRONMENT

8   *Portfolio Activity*

Collect information which explains the health and safety regulations of the work setting. You may have answered this as part of C1 number 15.

9   List FOUR potential indoor hazards and FOUR potential outdoor hazards in the work setting and explain how the effects of EACH of these hazards could be minimised.

....

....

....

....

....

....

....

....

....

....

....

....

....

....

Portfolio Activity
Describe how hazards are reported in your work setting. The relevant recording documentation may be included in your portfolio.

10

Portfolio Activity

Design a checklist for staff to use when carrying out routine safety checks. It should include details about:

(a) the building
(b) the equipment

Why is it important to carry out regular safety checks?

11   Explain why it is important to follow the manufacturer's instructions and the relevant safety standards when using equipment.

....

....

....

....

....

....

....

....

....

....

....

....

....

12

Portfolio Activity

Design a chart which shows the adult/child ratios at different ages for the following work settings:

(a) childminders with babies and pre-school children
(b) play groups

13   *Portfolio Activity*

Describe the safety rules and procedures for collecting children from the work setting. This should include reference to special circumstances.

Why is it important to maintain and use accurate records to contact parents in an emergency?

14   Describe the fire and emergency procedures that may be used in the work setting. Explain how the carers should react during the implementation of the procedures.

....

....

....

....

....

....

....

....

....

....

....

....

15&16   *Portfolio Activity*

Collect information which explains the health and safety regulations of the work setting. You may have answered this as part of C1 number 15.

Why is important to ensure that the regulations are displayed and communicated to other adults in the setting?

17   *Portfolio Activity*

Describe the policies and procedures of the work setting for handling and disposing of body fluids and waste material. The relevant documentation could be included in your portfolio.

18   *Portfolio Activity*

Design an information sheet that could be displayed in the work setting highlighting the priorities for treating a casualty and how to apply them.

19   *(a)* List the contents of a First-Aid kit which may be used in the work setting.

....

....

....

....

....

....

(b) Who should replenish the First-Aid kit?

....

....

....

(c) Why is it important check the contents of the First-Aid kit on a regular basis?

....

....

....

....

20   ***Portfolio Activity***

Plan and if possible, implement an outing for a child or group of children. The following should be included:

(a) *safety*
(b) *transport requirements*
(c) *appropriate clothing*
(d) *food*
(e) *equipment*

21   What would the child care and education worker do to ensure the safety of a child while travelling in a private car? The legal requirements should be included.

....

....

....

....

22   *(a)* Why is it important to keep a list of the children who are going on an outing?

....

....

....

....

(b) Why should the list be checked regularly?

....

....

....

....

....

RELATIONSHIPS

23   A child has been violently sick at playgroup. An adult is reassuring the child and calming the other children. An inexperienced member of staff joins the group and comments on the mess and smell.

(a) Why is the adult's reaction inappropriate in this situation?

....

....

....

(b) How would you manage the situation?

....

....

....

24   How can the child care and education worker convey information to a parent without causing alarm?

....

....

....

25   *(a)* Why is it important to adhere to the work setting regulations on child protection?

....

....

....

(b) Who should be the first person to be informed/consulted by a child care and education worker when child abuse is suspected?

....

....

26   Why is it important for the child care and education worker to inform his/her line manager of explanations of injuries given by the parent/carer?

....

....

....

....

....

....

....

....

....

....

....

....

....

27   *(a)* Where you may see possible injuries and abrasions on a child that may cause concern.

....

....

(b) If an injury is observed, when and how should it be reported?

....

....

28   Why is it important to involve parents/carers from the early stages of enquiries related to suspected injuries?

....

....

....

....

....

....

29   (a) Why is it essential to gain the permission of the line manager to take children off the premises?

....

....

....

....

....

....

(b) When is it appropriate to obtain parental permission to take the child off the premises?

....

....

....

....

....

....

M3 – Mandatory Unit CSC97EY

CONTRIBUTE TO THE ACHIEVEMENT OF ORGANISATIONAL REQUIREMENTS

DESCRIPTIONS OF KNOWLEDGE, UNDERSTANDING AND SKILLS

Development		Evidence method	Evidence reference
I	the value of development of the setting through training, consultation and the support of individuals and how this is effected M.3.2.5		

Equipment, Materials, Environment		Evidence method	Evidence reference
2	the importance of prioritising and managing time efficiently M.3.1.3, 4		
3	the importance of listening and recording information accurately M.3.1.1, 2, 3		
4	the importance of carrying out instructions as specified M.3.3.3, 6		
5	the value and potential of own contribution to the development of good practice M.3.2.1, 7		
6	current practice and objectives of the setting M.3.2.3		
7	the information sharing systems of the setting M.3.2.7		
8	how to receive directions and instructions M.3.2.6		

M3 – Mandatory Unit CSC97EY

CONTRIBUTE TO THE ACHIEVEMENT OF ORGANISATIONAL REQUIREMENTS

Relationships		Evidence method	Evidence reference
9	why and when to bring in or suggest the use of outside resources M.3.2.3		
10	how to share ideas with other people in the setting M.3.2.2, 7		
11	awareness of own role in the identification and development of good practice M.3.2.1, 2, 4		
12	awareness of own personal responsibility to follow through ideas and how to do it M.3.2.4		
13	awareness of own role in the evaluation of good practice M.3.2.1		
14	awareness of appropriate methods to help balance the needs of improving practice where unsatisfactory practice is currently being used M.3.2.6		
15	the importance of keeping to the boundaries of confidentiality as appropriate to the setting M.3.1.10; M3.2.8		

Grid M3

Please tick box when activity is complete:
P = Portfolio Activity

DEVELOPMENT	1		

EQUIPMENT, MATERIALS, ENVIRONMENT	2	3	4
	5	6	7
		P	7
	8		

RELATIONSHIPS	9	10	11
		P	P
	12	13	14
	P	P	
	15		

MANDATORY UNIT

M3 CONTRIBUTE TO THE ACHIEVEMENT OF ORGANISATIONAL REQUIREMENTS

Description of knowledge, understanding and skills

DEVELOPMENT

1   How can the work setting benefit:

(a) from receiving training from external agencies

....

....

....

....

....

....

(b) from talking to and visiting similar work settings

....

....

....

....

....

....

EQUIPMENT, MATERIALS, ENVIRONMENT

2-4   Why is it important to:

(a) prioritise and manage time efficiently

....

....

....

....

(b) listen to and record information accurately?

....

....

....

....

(c) carry out instructions given by another member of staff accurately?

....

....

....

....

5   How can you contribute to the good practice of the work setting?

....

....

....

....

....

6   *Portfolio Activity*

Design a leaflet for parents which outlines the aims and objectives of the work setting.

7   *Portfolio Activity*

Collect evidence of different ways in which the work setting shares information with parents and team members.

8   The line manager has given an inexperienced member of staff a list of detailed directions and instructions. What strategies could he/she use to ensure that the tasks are completed in a satisfactory way?

....

....

....

....

....

....

....

....

....

....

....

....

....

....

....

RELATIONSHIPS

9   When would it be appropriate for the work setting to suggest the use of
        outside resources? Give TWO different examples.

        ....

        ....

        ....

        ....

        ....

        ....

        ....

        Why would it be appropriate?

        ....

        ....

        ....

        ....

        ....

        ....

10   *Portfolio Activity*

        *Describe TWO different ways in which you have shared information with other people in
        the work setting.*

11-13   *Portfolio Activity*

        Your role within the workplace is very important.

        (a) How can you promote good practice?
        (b) Why is it important that you suggest ideas and follow them through?
        (c) What is your role in evaluating good practice?

14   You have observed unsatisfactory practice in the work setting. How would you manage the situation?

....

....

....

....

....

....

....

....

....

15   Why is it important to maintain confidentiality in the work setting?

....

....

....

....

....

....

....

....

....

P1 – Mandatory Unit CSC97EY

RELATE TO PARENTS

DESCRIPTIONS OF KNOWLEDGE, UNDERSTANDING AND SKILLS

Equipment, Materials Environment		Evidence method	Evidence reference
1	why it enhances the care and education of children to develop good relationships with their parents P.1.1.1		
2	types of information it is appropriate to pass to parents and which are beyond the candidate's area of responsibility P.1.1.3, 4		
3	the policy of the setting concerning confidentiality and understanding of the importance of safeguarding confidentiality of information P.1.1.9; P.1.2.5		
4	the policy and practice for settling-in of the setting and of arrangements made with parents P.1.2.3, 6		

Relationships		Evidence method	Evidence reference
5	feelings of some parents of apprehension, uncertainty or lack of confidence in relating to the candidate and the setting P.1.1.1		
6	understanding of why it is important to address people by the name and title which they prefer P.1.1.2		
7	parents' needs for regular information about their child's experiences in parents' absence in order to sustain continuity of care P.1.1.6, 7		
8	the central role played by parents in children's welfare and development P.1.1.1, 5		

P1 – Mandatory Unit CSC97EY

RELATE TO PARENTS

9	the importance of parental praise and encouragement in the activities of their child P.1.1.8		
10	understanding that family values and practices differ within cultural and other groupings as well as across such groups P.1.2.1, 2		

Grid P1

Please tick box when activity is complete:
P = Portfolio Activity

EQUIPMENT, MATERIALS, ENVIRONMENT	1	2	3
		P	
	4		
	P		

RELATIONSHIPS	5	6	7
			P
	8	9	10

MANDATORY UNIT

P1 RELATE TO PARENTS

Description of knowledge, understanding and skills

EQUIPMENT, MATERIALS, ENVIRONMENT

1   Why is it important to develop good relationships with the children's parents?

    ....

    ....

    ....

    ....

2   *Portfolio Activity*

    (a) List the type of information that may be given to parents throughout the week.
    (b) Identify the types of information that may be given to parents but are beyond your area of responsibility.

3   Find out about the policy of your work setting concerning confidentiality. Give reasons why it is important to safeguard confidentiality of information.

    ....

    ....

    ....

    ....

4   *Portfolio Activity*

    Describe the policies and practice of the work setting for settling-in of new children and the arrangements that are made with the parents.

RELATIONSHIPS

5   The child care and education worker has observed that a parent is very reluctant to come into the work setting. The parent appears to be very apprehensive and lacking in confidence.

(a) What reasons could the parent have for reacting in this way?

....

....

....

(b) How could the work setting help the parent overcome this anxiety?

....

....

....

6   Why is it important to address people using the name and title they prefer?

....

....

....

7   *Portfolio Activity*

Design a programme that will cater for parents' needs with regard to receiving regular information about their children.

8   Why is the role of the parent so important to the child's welfare and development?

....

....

....

....

9   Why is it important for the parent to encourage and praise the activities that the child does in the work setting?

....

....

....

....

....

....

....

....

....

10   Why is it important to recognise the different family values and practices that may be represented within the work setting?

....

....

....

....

....

....

....

....

....

C12 – Optional Unit CSC97EY

FEED BABIES

DESCRIPTIONS OF KNOWLEDGE, UNDERSTANDING AND SKILLS

Development		Evidence method	Evidence reference
1	a basic knowledge of the growth and development of babies up to 12 months and how this can be affected by the social, emotional and physical environment C12.3.2		
2	a general basic knowledge of the nutritional requirements of babies C12.1.5		
3	typical feeding requirements and patterns of feeding of babies at different developmental stages and how they may vary C12.2.1		
4	why some babies may have difficulties with feeding and how to overcome common difficulties C12.2.1, 10, 11		
5	the process of weaning and current medical advice on when weaning should be started C12.3.1, 7. 8		
6	cultural variations and approaches to feeding and weaning babies C12.1.6; C12.3.3		

Curriculum Practice		Evidence method	Evidence reference
7	the importance of interaction/communication with babies before, during and after feeding C12.2.8; C12.3.6		
8	different methods of cleaning feeding equipment C12.1.2		
9	the importance of winding and settling the baby after feeds and how this contributes to babies' welfare C12.2.7, 13		

C12 – Optional Unit CSC97EY

FEED BABIES

10	what constitutes a balanced diet for babies of different ages and how and when to introduce new foods C12.3.7, 8		
11	babies' need to experiment with feeds and feed themselves as part of growing independence C12.3.6, 7, 8		

Equipment, Materials, Environment		Evidence method	Evidence reference
12	the difference between sterilisation and social cleanliness, the principles of sterilisation and different methods of sterilisation C12.1.1, 2, 3, 4		
13	the importance of hygiene and how to maintain standards of hygiene acceptable to the setting C12.2.3, 9, 13; C12.3.3, 10		
14	the different types of milk required for cultural, religious or medical reasons C12.1.6		
15	methods of food preparation and associated hygiene and safety requirements C12.3.3		
16	the adverse effects if feeds are not properly made up C12.1.7		
17	different methods of heating made up feeds C12.1.7		
18	the methods and the storage properties of made up feeds to minimise deterioration C12.1.7, 8		
19	the importance of a suitable environment for feeding C12.2.5		
20	specialised equipment for babies with special needs and how and where to obtain it C12.2.11		

C12 – Optional Unit CSC97EY

FEED BABIES

21	relevance of vitamin supplements C12.3.7		
Relationships		Evidence method	Evidence reference
22	the importance of consultation between parents and the other carers and complying with parents' wishes over feeding routines C12.1.6; C12.3.3		

Grid C12

Please tick box when activity is complete:
P = Portfolio Activity

DEVELOPMENT	1	2	3
	P	P	
	4	5	6
		P	

CURRICULUM PRACTICE	7	8	9
	10	11	12
	P		P

EQUIPMENT, MATERIALS, ENVIRONMENT	13	14	15
	16	17	18
	19	20	21

RELATIONSHIPS	22		

C12 FEED BABIES

Description of knowledge, understanding and skills

DEVELOPMENT

1 **Portfolio Activity**

Design a booklet for parents which explains how a baby grows and develops from birth to 12 months. The booklet should explain how the baby's development is affected by the social, emotional and physical environment.

2 **Portfolio Activity**

Design a poster or leaflet for parents which explains the nutritional requirements of a baby up to 12 months old.

3 What are the feeding requirements of a baby:

(a) under 4 months of age

....

....

....

(b) over 4 months of age?

....

....

....

4   Why do some babies have difficulty feeding and how can the carer overcome these difficulties?

....

....

....

....

....

5   *Portfolio Activity*

Design a chart which shows how weaning on to solid food may progress. The following information should be included:

(a) age of baby
(b) nutritional requirements
(c) type of food
(d) taste and texture

6   Choose TWO different cultures. For EACH culture, briefly describe how babies are fed and weaned.

....

....

....

....

....

....

....

....

....

....

Curriculum Practice

7   Why is it important for the carer to talk to the baby before, during and after the baby has been fed?

       ....

       ....

       ....

       ....

       ....

       ....

8   Describe in detail TWO different methods of cleaning feeding equipment.

       ....

       ....

       ....

       ....

       ....

       ....

9   Why is it important to wind and settle the baby after the feed? How does this contribute to the baby's welfare?

       ....

       ....

       ....

       ....

       ....

       ....

10   ***Portfolio Activity***

Plan and implement where possible a balanced menu for one day for a six-month-old baby AND a twelve-month-old baby.

11   Describe ways in which the carer can encourage the baby to eat independently.

....

....

....

....

....

....

....

....

....

....

....

....

....

....

 12   ***Portfolio Activity***

Design a chart or leaflet which explains the importance of sterilisation. The chart should include:

(a) the different methods of sterilisation
(b) the importance of sterilisation
(c) how bacteria and infections are spread
(d) the possible effects of not sterilising equipment.

EQUIPMENT, MATERIALS, ENVIRONMENT

13   *(a)* Why is it important to ensure that the work setting is hygienic?

....

....

(b) Describe THREE practical ways in which the work setting can maintain high standards of hygiene.

....

....

14   Describe the different types of milk that may be required for:

(a) cultural reasons

....

....

(b) religious reasons

....

....

(c) medical reasons

....

....

15   Select THREE different types of food that may be given to a baby. Describe how EACH type of food should be prepared for a spoon feed.

....

....

....

....

16   What could happen if the formula feed is not prepared properly?

....

....

....

....

....

....

....

17   Describe TWO different ways of preparing formula feeds.

....

....

....

....

....

....

18   How should formula feeds be stored?

....

....

....

....

....

....

A carer has bought a manufactured formula feed. How long can it be kept for before being used?

....

....

....

....

....

....

A baby has not eaten a full portion of the formula feed that has been prepared. If this food is stored, what precautions should be taken to ensure that the food is safe to eat at a later stage?

....

....

....

....

....

....

19   Where should the baby be fed? Give THREE different examples with reasons for your choice.

....

....

....

....

....

....

20   A baby with special needs may require specialised feeding equipment. Give THREE examples of the type of equipment that may be necessary. Where could parents obtain the equipment from?

....

....

....

....

....

....

....

....

....

....

21   When should vitamin supplements be used when feeding a baby?

....

....

....

....

....

....

....

....

....

RELATIONSHIPS

22   Why is it important for the carer to discuss the feeding routines of the baby
with the parents?

....

....

....

....

....

....

....

....

....

....

....

....

....

....

....

....

....

Optional Unit CSC97EY – C13

PROVIDE FOR BABIES' PHYSICAL DEVELOPMENT NEEDS

DESCRIPTIONS OF KNOWLEDGE, UNDERSTANDING AND SKILLS

Development		Evidence method	Evidence reference
1	basic knowledge of child development all pcs in C13		
2	the importance of all the senses in stimulating development C13.3.1, 3, 5, 6		
3	the importance of communication and stimulation to the development of babies up to 12 months and awareness of the consequences of the lack of stimulation C13.2.9, 10; C13.3.1, 2, 3, 4		
4	how babies react to water at different ages and their individual differences and experiences C13.1.10		
5	the common skin conditions and variations in bowel and bladder action which need to be reported C13.2.8		
6	possible unusual conditions and reactions which should be reported C13.1.11		
7	when and how to provide appropriate assistance to encourage walking C13.3.7		

Curriculum Practice		Evidence method	Evidence reference
8	the importance of washing as a sensory and pleasurable experience for babies C13.1.14		
9	appropriate toys and equipment to stimulate babies from 0–12 months C13.3.1, 5		

Optional Unit CSC97EY – C13

PROVIDE FOR BABIES' PHYSICAL DEVELOPMENT NEEDS

10	the importance of communication and stimulation to the development of babies up to 12 months all C13.3		
11	cultural differences in toileting and hygiene procedures C13.2.5		
12	why different parts of babies' bodies are washed differently C13.1.9		

Equipment, Materials, Environment		Evidence method	Evidence reference
13	the general health and safety requirements of the setting and for babies at different ages up to 12 months C13.1.1, 2, 8, 13		
14	health and safety procedures necessary to protect the worker from infection and how to use them C13.1.7, 13		
15	the range and suitability of washing equipment and toiletries C13.1.3, 6		
16	the importance of a safe, clean environment for babies C13.2.1, 2, 5		
17	different types of nappies and how to apply them according to age and gender of babies C13.2.5		
18	the range and suitability of clothing C13.2.11		
19	range, application and suitability of toiletries C13.2.4		
20	suitable safety equipment for use with babies of different ages and stages of development C13.3.8		

Optional Unit CSC97EY – C13

PROVIDE FOR BABIES' PHYSICAL DEVELOPMENT NEEDS

21	the importance of maintaining standards of hygiene and cleanliness for clothing and nursery equipment for babies C13.4.2		
22	cleaning and disinfectant materials suitable for baby clothing and nursery equipment and how to use them safely C13.4.1, 6		
23	appropriate laundry methods/techniques for different types of materials C13.4.3		
24	simple repair techniques C13.4.7		
Relationships		Evidence method	Evidence reference
25	the importance of listening to parents' wishes and advice about washing their babies C13.1.4		
26	the importance of parents knowing about the activities experienced by their babies C13.3.9		

Grid C13

Please tick box when activity is complete:
P = Portfolio Activity

DEVELOPMENT	1	2	3
	P		
	4	5	6
	P		
	7		

CURRICULUM PRACTICE	8	9	10
	11	12	

EQUIPMENT, MATERIALS, ENVIRONMENT	13	14	15
		P	**P**
	16	17	18
	19	20	21
	P		
	22	23	24

RELATIONSHIPS	25	26	

OPTIONAL UNIT

C13 PROVIDE FOR BABIES' PHYSICAL DEVELOPMENT NEEDS

Description of knowledge, understanding and skills

DEVELOPMENT

1   ***Portfolio Activity***

Design a booklet for parents which explains how a baby grows and develops from birth to 12 months. The booklet should explain how the baby's development is affected by the social, emotional and physical environment. (You may have completed this work for C12.1)

2   Why is it important to develop the senses of a baby?

....

....

....

....

3   Why is it important for the adult to communicate with and stimulate the baby?

....

....

....

....

4

Portfolio Activity

Observe a baby aged between birth and six months having a bath. Describe how the baby reacted to the water.
Observe a baby aged between 6 months and one year having a bath. Describe how the baby reacted to the water. Compare his/her reactions with your observations of the younger baby.

5   Name and describe a skin condition which may be observed when changing a baby's nappy.

....

....

....

....

....

Describe any variations in bowel and/or bladder control which may need to be reported to the carer.

....

....

....

....

....

6   Describe an unusual condition or reaction from a baby which should be reported by the carer.

....

....

....

....

7   When and how should the carer encourage a baby to walk?

....

....

....

....

....

....

....

....

....

....

....

....

....

....

....

....

....

....

....

....

CURRICULUM PRACTICE

8   Why is it important to make bathtime a pleasurable experience for babies?

....

....

....

....

....

....

9   You have been asked by a parent to recommend a selection of toys that would be suitable for a baby during the first year of his/her life. What would you suggest and why?

....

....

....

....

....

....

10   Why is it important for the adult to communicate with and stimulate the baby?

....

....

....

....

....

11   Describe the cultural differences which may occur in toilet training and hygienic procedures.

....

....

....

....

....

....

....

....

....

....

12   Explain why different parts of the baby's body are bathed separately.

....

....

....

....

....

....

....

....

....

....

EQUIPMENT, MATERIALS, ENVIRONMENT

13   Describe the health and safety requirements of babies aged between:

(a) birth and 4 weeks

....

....

(b) 1 month and 3 months

....

....

(c) 4 months and 6 months

....

....

(d) 6 months and a year

....

....

14   *Portfolio Activity*

Design a poster which explains to carers how to protect themselves from infection when working with babies.

15   *Portfolio Activity*

Design a leaflet which shows a range of bathing equipment and toiletries. Write short notes to explain the suitability of the equipment.

16   Why is it important to ensure that the work setting is safe and clean?

....

....

17   Describe the different types of nappies that are available for boys and girls and explain how to use them.

....

....

18   Describe the range and suitability of clothing for a baby aged between birth and 12 months.

....

....

19   *Portfolio Activity*

Design a leaflet for parents which shows the range and suitability of toiletries for a baby. Provide brief instructions on how to use the toiletries.

20   What safety equipment could you buy for:

(a) a cooker

....

....

(b) electric sockets

....

....

(c) a bath

....

....

(d) doors and cupboard

....

....

....

21   Why is it important to ensure that a baby's clothes and nursery equipment are clean and hygienic?

....

....

....

....

....

....

22   Complete the table below:

Cleaning materials and disinfectants	How to use them safely
1	
2	
3	
4	
5	

23   How would you wash the following materials?

(a) wool

....

....

(b) cotton

....

....

....

....

(c) nylon

....

....

....

....

24   A button has become loose on a baby's jumper. How should this be repaired? Why is it important to repair it?

....

....

....

....

A baby's wooden brick has splinters. How should this be repaired?

....

....

....

....

....

RELATIONSHIPS

25   Why is it important to listen to the parent's wishes and advice about washing their babies?

....

....

....

....

....

....

....

....

....

26   Why is it important to inform the parent of the activities the baby has experienced during the day at the work setting?

....

....

....

....

....

....

....

....

Optional Unit CSC97EY – M1

MONITOR, STORE AND PREPARE MATERIALS AND EQUIPMENT

	DESCRIPTIONS OF KNOWLEDGE, UNDERSTANDING AND SKILLS		
	Equipment, Materials, Environment	Evidence method	Evidence reference
1	the procedures of the setting for dealing with faults in equipment M.1.1.6		
2	operating procedures and safety requirements of the setting regarding use of equipment M.1.1.4, 5		
3	how to use equipment following manufacturers' instructions M.1.1.1		
4	accessories and spare parts required for different types of equipment M.1.1.7		
5	what to do if equipment breaks down M.1.2.5		
6	how to operate equipment M.1.2.4		
7	the procedures of the setting for dealing with shortfalls in materials M.1.2.6; M.1.3.7		
8	health and safety requirements of the setting for storage and use of materials M.1.2.6; M.1.3.1		
9	materials which may deteriorate and how to prevent or delay this M.1.3.5		
10	how to record stock levels M.1.3.4, 6		

Grid M1

Please tick box when activity is complete:
P = Portfolio Activity

	1	2	3
	P	**P**	**P**
	4	5	6
EQUIPMENT, MATERIALS, ENVIRONMENT			
	7	8	9
	P		
	10		
	P		

OPTIONAL UNIT

M1 MONITOR, STORE AND PREPARE MATERIALS AND EQUIPMENT

Description of knowledge, understanding and skills

EQUIPMENT, MATERIALS, ENVIRONMENT

 1 **Portfolio Activity**

Describe the procedures used by the work setting for reporting AND dealing with faults to equipment. You may want to include the relevant forms in your portfolio.

 2 **Portfolio Activity**

Design a booklet for staff in the work setting which explains the operating procedures AND safety requirements for EACH of the following pieces of equipment:

(a) cassette recorder/player
(b) video recorder/player
(c) overhead projector
(d) computer

 3 **Portfolio Activity**

Set up EACH of the pieces of equipment given in (2) according to the manufacturers instructions. Describe how effective you were.

4 For EACH of the pieces of equipment named in (2) provide a list of accessories and spare parts that may be required.

....

....

....

5   Explain the procedures used in the work setting when the reprographic equipment breaks down.

....

....

....

6   Describe how to operate reprographic equipment.

....

....

....

7   *Portfolio Activity*

Describe the procedures of the work setting when there are insufficient materials available for use. You may include the appropriate documentation in your portfolio.

8   Describe the health and safety requirements for the storage AND use of EACH of the items listed below.

(a) Art and craft materials:
*   paints (different types of paints should be included)

....

....

....

....

*   glue and paste

....

....

....

....

- clay

....

....

- paper (different types of paper and their purpose should be included)

....

....

(b) Play and learning materials
- sand

....

....

- wood

....

....

- dough

....

....

(NB Other materials not mentioned above may be included in the portfolio.)

9   From the list given above, list the materials which will deteriorate and explain how the deterioration of EACH material may be delayed or prevented.

....

....

....

....

10

Portfolio Activity

Design one or more checklists which may be used in the work setting to record the stock levels of the following equipment:

(a) art and craft material
(b) cleaning materials
(c) stationery

Optional Unit CSC97EY – P9

WORK WITH PARENTS IN A GROUP

DESCRIPTIONS OF KNOWLEDGE, UNDERSTANDING AND SKILLS

Equipment, Materials, Environment		Evidence method	Evidence reference
1	sources of help in the case of communication difficulties P.9.1.2, 3		
2	the benefits to the group, the parents and the children of parents' involvement in the group P.9.2.2, 3, 4		
3	ways in which parents' skills can help the group and enable them to join in children's activities P.9.2.2, 3; P.9.3.3, 4		
4	different ways of stimulating parents' interest in children's activities P.9.3.1, 4		

Relationships		Evidence method	Evidence reference
5	how to communicate with parents as equals and how to listen to parents P.9.1.1, 2		
6	the boundaries of responsibility for work with parents and to whom enquiries beyond these should be referred P.9.1.6		
7	how family lifestyles, approaches to child rearing and play vary with family background and culture P.9.1.2, 5		
8	possible barriers to parents' participation in the group P.9.2.1; P.9.3.4, 6, 7		
9	the reasons why some parents are reluctant to participate in children's activities P.9.3.5		

Optional Unit CSC97EY – P9

WORK WITH PARENTS IN A GROUP

Curriculum Practice	Evidence method	Evidence reference
10 the nature and purpose of children's activities P.9.3.2		

Grid P9

Please tick box when activity is complete:
P = Portfolio Activity

	1	2	3
EQUIPMENT, MATERIALS, ENVIRONMENT			
	4		
	P		

	5	6	7
RELATIONSHIPS	P		
	8	9	10
			P

P9 WORK WITH PARENTS IN A GROUP

Description of knowledge, understanding and skills

EQUIPMENT, MATERIALS, ENVIRONMENT

1   Where could you get help from when communicating with parents who have:

   (a) hearing difficulties

   ....

   ....

   ....

   ....

   (b) language barriers

   ....

   ....

   ....

   ....

2   What are the benefits of parents becoming involved in the work of the group?

   ....

   ....

   ....

3   Parents have skills which can be of value to the work setting. List FIVE ways in
           which parents may be able to contribute to the work of the setting.

           ....

           ....

           ....

           ....

           ....

           ....

           ....

           ....

           ....

4   *Portfolio Activity*

           *Select THREE activities that you would plan for your children. For EACH activity
           describe ways of stimulating the parent's interest in the children's activities.*

RELATIONSHIPS

5   *Portfolio Activity*

You have been asked to give a short talk (between 5 and 10 minutes) to a student nursery nurse at the local college on how to communicate with and listen to parents. Write or tape the talk that you would give.

6   Describe the responsibilities that different members of staff have when working with parents e.g. pre-school leader, parent helper, trainee etc.

....

....

....

....

....

Who should staff go to for help if the situation is beyond their responsibility?

....

....

....

....

....

7   Choose TWO different cultures and describe the family lifestyles, including play and child rearing.

....

....

....

....

....

8   What factors could prevent parents participating in the work of the setting?

....

....

....

....

....

....

....

....

....

....

9   Why do some parents find it difficult to participate in the children's activities? Your answer should relate to real situations wherever possible. Confidentiality must be maintained at all times.

....

....

....

....

....

....

....

....

....

CURRICULUM PRACTICE

10   ***Portfolio Activity***

Design a booklet for parents which includes the following information:

(a) the activities that are available to the children in the work setting and the way in which the activities promote the development of the child

(b) practical ways in which the parents can participate in the children's activities.

CU10 – Optional Unit CSC97CA

CONTRIBUTE TO THE EFFECTIVENESS OF WORK TEAMS

DESCRIPTIONS OF KNOWLEDGE, UNDERSTANDING AND SKILLS

Knowledge Specification for the Whole of this Unit
You must show your assessor that you know and understand the following:
(the numbers after each knowledge statement refer to performance criteria)

Legislation, Policy and Good Practice

		Evidence method	Evidence reference
1	What effective communication is CU10.1		
2	Why one should take responsibility for one's own development and performance and the contribution of this to learning and development itself CU10.2.4		

Factors Which Influence What You Do

		Evidence method	Evidence reference
3	Why it is not always possible to evaluate one's own performance, strengths and weakness and the role which others' feedback plays CU10.2.3		
4	The effects of differing cultures on communications (such as the use of touch, presence, contact-distance between individuals when communicating, the terms of respect used etc.) CU10.1		
5	The constraints to effective communication [environmental e.g. noise and light: social/cultural e.g. language, jargon, slang, dialect; interpersonal; individual's psychological, social and emotional well-being] CU10.1		

CU10 – Optional Unit CSC97CA

CONTRIBUTE TO THE EFFECTIVENESS OF WORK TEAMS

6	Barriers to developing relationships and how these can be overcome CU10.1.8		
7	The range of problems which one may encounter when inter-relating with others and how these can best be handled CU10.1.9		
8	Your role in relation to others in the work team CU10.1.2; CU10.1.5		
9	The role of others within the team and how each interacts CU10.1.7; CU10.2		
10	The range of interactive styles which individuals have and how these may effect ongoing work CU10.1.2		
11	The differences between work and personal relationships and how work relationships can be maintained effectively even if one has little in common outside of work CU10.1.2		
12	The effects which work priorities have on individuals and how it may be possible to offer help and support CU10.1.3		
13	When, and when not, to interrupt others during work and the effects which this may have on them CU10.1.6		
14	The busy and stressful times within the work team and how these can best be handled CU10.1.6		
15	Development routes which may be open and those which may be suitable CU10.2.4		

CU10 – Optional Unit CSC97CA

CONTRIBUTE TO THE EFFECTIVENESS OF WORK TEAMS

16	Your personal career goals and the relationship of these to current work CU10.2.2		
17	Your own strengths and weaknesses and how the former can be built on and the latter minimised CU10.2.1		
18	The potential obstacles to personal development CU10.2.4		

How to Achieve Important Outcomes		Evidence method	Evidence reference
19	Methods of establishing and developing constructive relationships with others CU10.1.2		
20	Methods of communicating clearly and effectively CU10.1.1		
21	Methods of handling and minimising inter-personal conflict CU10.1.8		
22	How to identify and recognise one's own competence CU10.2.1		
23	How practice is changing and the effects of these changes on the worker CU10.2.2		
24	How to review one's own progress with others effectively and encourage them to give constructive feedback CU10.2.3, CU10.2.5		

Grid CU10

Please tick box when activity is complete:
P = Portfolio Activity

LEGISLATION, POLICY AND GOOD PRACTICE	1	2	

	3	4	5
	6	7	8
			P
	9	10	11
FACTORS WHICH INFLUENCE WHAT YOU DO	P	P	
	12	13	14
			P
	15	16	17
	P	P	P
	18		
	P		

HOW TO ACHIEVE IMPORTANT OUTCOMES	19	20	20
	P		
	22	23	24
		P	P

OPTIONAL UNIT

CU10 CONTRIBUTE TO THE EFFECTIVENESS OF WORK TEAMS

Description of knowledge, understanding and skills

LEGISLATION, POLICY AND GOOD PRACTICE

1   List FIVE different ways to communicate information.

        ....

        ....

        ....

        ....

        ....

        Describe what is meant by 'effective communication'.

        ....

        ....

        ....

        ....

        ....

        ....

        ....

2   Why is it important for you to take responsibility for your own learning and development?

....

....

....

....

....

....

....

....

....

....

....

....

....

....

....

....

....

....

....

FACTORS WHICH INFLUENCE WHAT YOU DO

3   A nursery nurse student has been completing his practical training in the work
     setting. He thought he was doing well but when he received his final report he
     had achieved a number of very low grades.

   (a) What factors may have led him to believe that he was doing well?

   ....

   ....

   ....

   ....

   (b) How could the situation have been prevented?

   ....

   ....

   ....

   ....

   It may be useful to discuss this question with a colleague before answering it.

4   Choose TWO different cultures. Describe how people from EACH culture
     communicate with each other. You should consider the use of touch,
     presence, contact-distance between individuals.

   ....

   ....

   ....

   ....

   ....

   ....

   ....

5   What could hinder effective communication? Give TWO reasons for each of the headings shown in the table below:

    ....

    ....

    ....

    ....

    ....

What can hinder effective communication	
Environmental Factors	
Language Barriers	

6   Name THREE barriers which could affect a developing relationship. Explain how each barrier could be overcome.

    ....

    ....

    ....

    ....

    ....

    ....

    ....

    ....

7   The following difficulties may arise when working with people. Briefly describe
        how you would manage each situation:

        (a) bullying

        ....

        ....

        ....

        ....

        (b) personality clashes

        ....

        ....

        ....

        ....

        (c) discrimination

        ....

        ....

        ....

        ....

8&9   ***Portfolio Activity***

        (a) Describe your role in the work setting in relation to other members of the team.
        (b) Describe the role of the other members of the team in your work setting. Explain how
        *   each role interacts with each other.*

        If you work on your own, you should consider the other adults you work with e.g.
        parents, other professionals etc.

10   ***Portfolio Activity***

        Before you begin this activity it is essential to ask the other team members if you may carry
        out the task. Confidentiality is essential.

        Observe a meeting in the work setting. How does each member of the team interact with
        his/her colleagues?

11   *(a)* What is the difference between work and personal relationships?

....

....

     (b) Although members of the team may have little in common outside work, what common factors do each member of the team have when working together?

....

....

12   *(a)* What effect can work priorities have on colleagues?

....

....

     (b) How can other members of the team help?

....

....

13   When would you interrupt a colleague during work? Give TWO examples.

....

....

....

When would you not interrupt a colleague during work? Give TWO examples.

....

....

....

....

14   *Portfolio Activity*

   (a) Briefly describe the weekly routine of your work setting.
   (b) Identify the busy and stressful times in the week.
   (c) Select TWO particularly busy or stressful times and suggest ways in which they may be altered to reduce the tension that may arise.

 15-18   *Portfolio Activity*

   Design a personal development plan. It should include:

   (a) a brief description of what you have achieved to date
   (b) your strengths and weaknesses
   (c) suggestions on how you may use your strengths to improve your weaknesses
   (d) a plan which shows how your career can progress. This may include different qualifications and types of employment
   (e) your own personal career goals
   (f) any obstacles that may prevent you achieving your goals.

HOW TO ACHIEVE IMPORTANT OUTCOMES

19   *Portfolio Activity*

Describe how you established and developed good working relationships with your colleagues.

20   How can the child care and education worker communicate clearly and effectively? Give THREE practical examples.

....

....

....

....

21   A member of staff has offended a colleague and as a result they are not speaking to each other except when it is absolutely necessary. How can this situation be managed and how can it be prevented from happening again?

....

....

....

....

22   How can a child care and education worker identify what he/she has been able to achieve when working with young children?

....

....

....

....

....

23   *Portfolio Activity*

Describe TWO important changes that have occurred in your work setting over the last few months. What effects have each of these changes had on the team?

 24   *Portfolio Activity*

Arrange an interview with your line manager to discuss your progress over a period of time. Ask your line manager to give you constructive feedback on your performance. You may want to include this information in your personal development plan that you completed for CU 15–18.